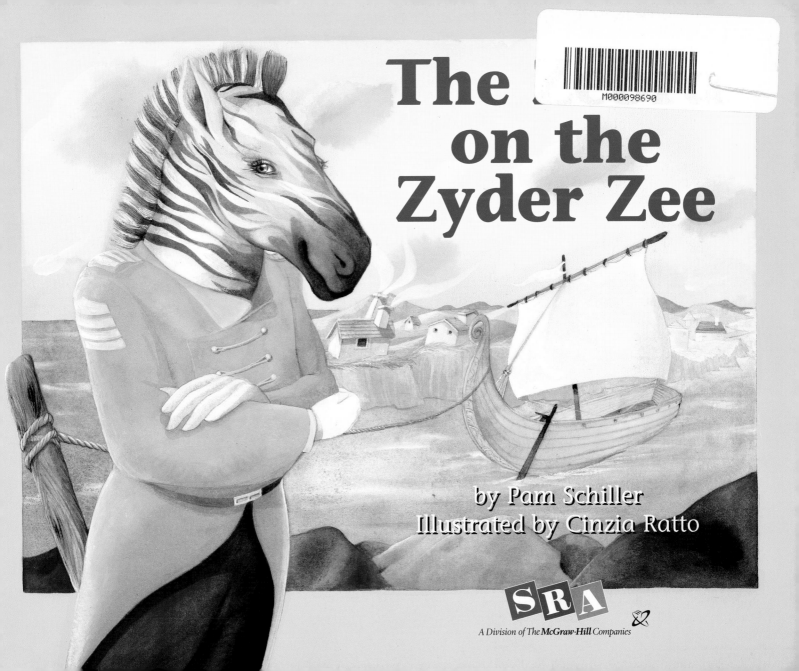

# The
# on the
# Zyder Zee

by Pam Schiller

Illustrated by Cinzia Ratto

SRA

A Division of The McGraw·Hill Companies

**www.sra4kids.com**

*SRA/McGraw-Hill*

*A Division of The* **McGraw·Hill** *Companies*

Send all inquiries to:
SRA/McGraw-Hill
8787 Orion Place
Columbus, OH  43240-4027

Printed in the United States of America.

ISBN  0-07-572411-1

3 4 5 6 7 8 9 QST 06 05 04 03

The Zebra on the Zyder Zee
Wanted to sail across the sea.
He called to his friends 1, 2, 3,
"Come along and sail with me."

The Zebra on the Zyder Zee
Said, "I am lonesome, don't you see.
I want to sail across the sea,
But I simply must have company."

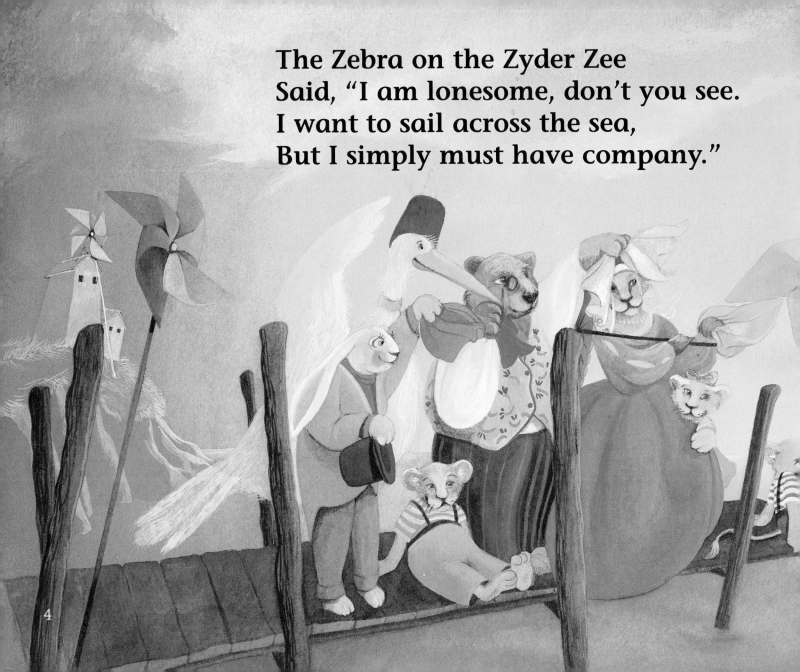

The first to come on the Zyder Zee
Was the Zebra's friend Sir Ronnee Ree.
He said, "I'll be your company.
I'd love to sail across the sea."

The next to come to the Zyder Zee
Was Elizabeth Holleque de Dundee.
She brought her little urchins three
And said, "Let's sail across the sea."

8

The Zebra on the Zyder Zee
Was just as happy as he could be.
He was going to sail across the sea,
And the Zyder Zee had company.

He hoisted the sails 1, 2, 3,
And the friends were off to see the sea.
Day and night and day times three,
The jolly mates sailed across the sea.

The little ship rocked on the sea.
The jolly mates ate bread and brie.
The little ones sipped cinnamon tea,
And the Zebra sailed the Zyder Zee.

15

Day by day Ronnee studied the sea,
While Elizabeth read her poetry.
The urchins played Tic-tac-three
And the Zebra sailed the Zyder Zee.

16

When nighttime fell across the sea,
Elizabeth sang to the urchins three.
And her new friend, Sir Ronnee Ree,
Hummed along in harmony.

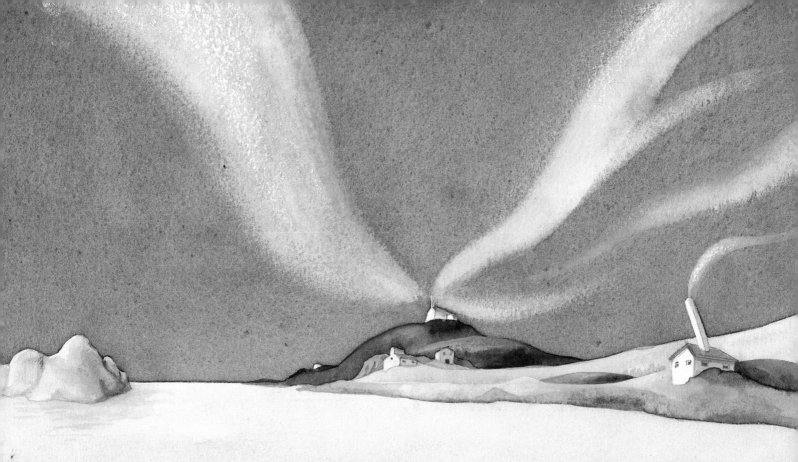

At last, the journey across the sea
Came to an end at half past three.
The Zebra and his company
Had finally sailed across the sea.

The little ones and Ms. Dundee
Took the hand of Ronnee Ree
And left the deck of the Zyder Zee,
Saying good-bye to the deep blue sea.

The Zebra cleaned the Zyder Zee
And lowered the sails 1, 2, 3.
He polished the decks merrily,
And dreamed of sailing back to sea.